Come On In

TO OUR WORLD OF LIVING with
VASCULAR DEMENTIA

VICKY DONOGHUE & MICHELLE SPRATT

Cover image by: Yonathan Kurniawan
Book design by: SWATT Books Ltd

Printed in the United Kingdom
First Printing, 2022

ISBN: 978-1-7392396-0-2 (Paperback)
ISBN: 978-1-7392396-1-9 (eBook)

Forget-Me-Not Publishing
Wokingham, Berkshire

In loving memory of John who we remember as a devoted husband, and a wonderful, caring dad and grandad.

TABLE OF CONTENTS

COME ON IN

1. FREEDOM

Freedom is a gift to be cherished; we take it for granted until it is stolen from us. Freedom allows you to be the person you really are. This is the story of how vascular dementia stole that freedom from my husband, John, destroyed my life and damaged our family. So many people think of dementia as a condition that affects the elderly and makes them forgetful. The truth is, dementia can strike at any time, and its effects on the person and their family can be shattering.

John had a personality that captured the room and everyone's hearts. 'Come on in,' would echo throughout the house whenever John opened our front door to our family and friends. How sad it was, in future years, when John would show such hospitality to unscrupulous sales people who were only too happy to prey on the vulnerable.

Dementia showed its true colours to our family as the cruel disease it is, that dismantles the personality and destroys the lives of those who love them as they endure the agony of watching the afflicted person slowly fade away. My daughter, Michelle, and I, have written this book to offer comfort to the relatives of other victims of this devastating disease. We want you to know you are not alone and we hope that our experiences will support you on your journey and that the tips we share with you will help you as you find your own way to cope.

We would like to commence our story with a tribute to John, the most loving husband, dad and grandad, by sharing a few of our fond memories of the most remarkable man, from the times when he still had his freedom.

John Robert Pascal Donoghue was born in Dublin, Ireland in January 1942, moving to England with his family in 1961. As a young boy John was an altar boy, singing in the church choir, making his Roman Catholic family proud. He had a musical talent, playing the guitar, violin and piano accordion and he was a keen member of the Irish dancing class at school.

He was raised with strong moral views which he held throughout his life; John would do anything for anyone. His core values of respect, love, humility, responsibility and spirituality formed a strong foundation for our marriage and family life. Everyone loved John with his friendly easy-going personality. He showed an interest in everyone he met, honouring them by remembering their names from the second he was introduced. People used to say he would have made a good counsellor with his listening ear.

John was a bit of a comedian; the room would be filled with laughter when he was present. Sitting watching television on an evening, we would often end up giggling at programmes, such as, 'The Last of The Summer Wine,' 'Open All Hours,' and 'Carry on Camping'. John would laugh hysterically at characters such as Kenny Everett and Benny Hill and other natural comics. In fact, John spent most of his time laughing, rather like his beloved mum who also had a fun sense of humour! He'd love to join in with games and quizzes and threw himself whole-heartedly into activities at family gatherings.

Michelle fondly recalls how, every Christmas, strings full of Christmas cards overtook the whole of the downstairs because we had so many friends; all of us knew it was John's magnetic personality which drew them to us.

John's flamboyant nature matched the effervescence of the Italians; we enjoyed several memorable holidays to Italy. He had an appreciation for fine architecture and had a passion for exploring the many beautiful churches and cathedrals, and in particular, the Sistine Chapel in Rome.

When he lived in Dublin, John had studied for an Engineering apprenticeship. He initially took on a role for the London Electricity Board before moving to Transport for London, (TfL). It was only a couple of years before he was asked to take on a managerial role in the safety and quality engineering team. John threw himself into the training to become a lecturer. For 32 years John put his heart and soul into his work with TfL, travelling daily into London by train, until his redundancy in 1996 when TfL restructured.

Such long service with the same company is an achievement worth shouting about. Another amazing thing John did, for more than 30 years, was that he donated blood, recognising that his kind generosity could help to save lives.

Dancing and music introduced John and I to each other in an Irish dance hall. When we met, I was with two friends and he kept looking over at me, before he came over and we enjoyed a dance together. I was 18 when we met, John was 22. A couple of years later, wedding bells rang for us on 11th March 1967. My parents were very fond of John, welcoming him into our family. We initially lived with John's lovely mum for a few years before we decided to move from London to the County of Hampshire, where we raised our three children. How quickly the joyous years passed; who would have believed that in the twinkle of an eye we would have six adorable grandchildren!

John was a spontaneous man, who would get out of bed one sunny morning and announce, 'Shall we go to Bournemouth for the day?' His active mind was always full of bright ideas. John liked to tinker; he loved nothing more than to join the neighbours under the bonnet of an old Ford as they fixed the engine together, and many friends relied greatly on his doing odd jobs for them.

Michelle remembers how she would often sit together with her dad on a Sunday afternoon to watch a Hammer House of Horror or Jaws film and how they both loved it! She also recalls her dad being engrossed in a daily newspaper each morning. He enjoyed television programmes about Fred Dibnah, the Bolton steeplejack, and was fascinated by films about World War 11 and submarines.

Not only did John love to watch, 'Carry on Camping,' but he loved taking us all on camping holidays where his friendly, magnetic personality ensured that we constantly had a stream of new friends. We went to lots of places, like Devon, Cornwall, The Isle of Wight, and Norfolk, with our trailer tent and sometimes to the ready erected tents at Eurocamp in France. He'd lead us on countryside rambles and always ensured that there were fun activities to occupy our time.

His organisational skills were greatly appreciated by the Southern Region Trailer Tent Group where he became chairman. John's leadership qualities made him an excellent master of ceremonies during our camping weekends. Michelle fondly remembers our trailer tent full of happy campers as they all flocked to mum and dad on an evening for a glass of homemade wine and a good laugh around the tiny dining table.

During our camping days we would engage in annual carnival parades and fundraising activities to raise money for the war veterans. Each year the procession supported a different theme, and the whole family and all the campers would look forward to an event full of fun and colour as we dressed up as characters from popular TV programmes, including The Flintstones, Batman and Robin, and St. Trinian's.

John's favourite past times were cycling, cars, walking, squash rackets, all types of dancing, especially country line dancing. He also enjoyed a game of swing ball, tennis and football in the park with the children.

Everybody loved snow days with dad. Michelle remembers dad being the first outside, building snowmen, followed by sledging down the nearby hills with neighbours and friends. Snowball ambushes, snow angels, daring sledging runs, hilarious crashes and meeting new friends always made for fun snowy days.

We took up line dancing as a hobby, and within a short space of time, we came to love the freedom of expression that line dancing gave us. John's love for country music and line dancing led him to teaching it. Everyone was amazed by his ability to memorize the intricate steps. Michelle recalls the numerous times she'd enter the lounge to find him rehearsing the steps. He made it all seem so easy. John and I worked together, as a team, leading the classes which welcomed all ages and abilities, and even the Brownies, Guides and students all loved learning something new. John thrived on seeing the delight on everyone's faces as they all became addicted to their new hobby! He always dressed the part too and wore lovely stetsons, beautiful shirts and leather bolo ties.

We would take his mum and her friend shopping every Friday, and we helped to organise a dance for her 90th birthday in her residential home, taking sequence dancers in to perform. How they loved it! We would also organise regular line dancing charity evenings in our local town, as well as teaming up with four good friends, to help run an annual camping and line dancing weekend, in aid of a children's charity, and which was a success for ten years. Of course, John was centre of attention as Master of Ceremonies at all these events.

John and I did everything together, enjoying every minute of each other's company. However, he also loved going for a drink with the lads, and he was forever Mr Popular with the ladies too, always willing to offer them a bear hug!

Michelle recalls, I have never forgotten my first visit to the cinema. It was the first time I can remember dad taking me out without mum and my two younger brothers. He took me to see 101 Dalmatians. Dad loved going to the cinema, and all types of theatre shows. We went on family outings to see a pantomime every year, which we all loved, and it has become a tradition with our children too.

These precious memories are just a few that we all treasure. It was so painful to observe as slowly John was robbed of them.

John and Vicky's wedding day, 11th March 1967.

John and Michelle on Eastbourne beach.

Family fun on the beach.

John cuddling Michelle, Nick and Mark.

All dressed up for the Flintstones carnival charity event.

… and the St. Trinian's carnival charity event.

Family fun in the snow with Dad's help.

More fun in the snow with Dad's help.

Celebrating John's Mum's 90th birthday.

All ready to teach the line dancing.

All lined up for the charity line-dance.

John always enjoyed washing the car.

Holiday fun at the Moulin Rouge.

2. A THIEF IN THE NIGHT

John's vascular dementia crept upon us like a thief in the night. Like the odd stray wave on the beach which heralds the incoming tide we would notice a trait, so out of character, that we would question ourselves. Did John really say or do that? John was in his late 50's so we didn't, in our wildest nightmares, consider dementia. We were more prepared to think that we were having our own 'dipsy do,' rather than think John, with his razor-sharp memory could have had such an out of character moment. Did he really repeat himself? He always seemed to be losing things! We questioned our own behaviour; had we done or said something to receive such a paranoid and combative reaction?

Things appeared out of character at first, for example, at a regular line dancing class, John complained to one of the students, 'Keep your noise down, I'm trying to teach a class here!' He would never have been bothered about something like that previously. His personality was changing, particularly when he made the abrupt decision to quit teaching people to dance. He began to lose concentration when we watched the television together. Looking back, I think I was in denial when I would return from making a cup of tea, to discover he couldn't tell me what had happened in the programme while I was out of the room. I found myself finishing his sentences when he couldn't remember the words.

He decided he'd like to drive a delivery van for a local supermarket and seemed to successfully deliver the goods, until one day he returned home with the van still full of customer deliveries, in our home town where he once would have known all the streets like the back of his hand! At this point I knew there was something seriously amiss.

The postman seemed to be forever hammering on our door with deliveries of cameras, tools, watches, shoes, clothes, and even vitamin pills, all ordered via mail order catalogues. We could have opened our own shop as the packages piled up in the hallway!

John had a passion for cars and his own always shone, spotless and polished; he had so much pride that the minutest scratch would have distressed him. He was a careful driver so we were all utterly dumbfounded the evening he arrived home and casually remarked that he had driven into a central reservation bollard in the nearby village. The significant damage to his beloved car did not seem to bother him at all and we thought, at first, that he was joking! He stopped washing the car, and mowing the grass, but we just thought that he was getting lazy.

We were equally speechless when John arrived home one day carrying a bundle of coats and jackets which he proudly claimed were 'designer.' We discovered that a mysterious con-artist had persuaded John to give him three different debit cards and pin numbers. John had stood by the ATM while £600 was taken from his accounts to pay for the large bundle of fake designer clothing.

While I was at work cold callers pounced. John accepted repeat visits from double glazing salesmen. Three utility suppliers, on different occasions, were among the salesmen whom I discovered as I returned home from work. I was outraged by these rogues, who had ignored the 'no cold callers' signs on our front door and were routing through our private financial paperwork. How difficult it was for me to cancel the various contracts which John had signed. I spent endless hours on the telephone attempting to rectify those frustrating incidents.

He began to forget the names of people and objects. The odd 'thingamabob,' and 'thingamajig,' in place of a name became all too common that, finally, we became alerted to the fact that something wasn't quite right with John's health, rather than dismiss these unusual episodes as our own misinterpretations. John struggled to participate in conversations, and in some ways, it was a blessing that we were totally ignorant of this wicked disease and unaware of things to come.

Michelle reminded us of the man who was fading away before our eyes. He was always excited to see people and would welcome them in to our family home with open arms. If I had friends over, he'd say —'Come on in my darling.' Dad was fun, intelligent and witty: always a bundle of positive energy. To my brothers and I growing up – he was a rock and an inspiration.

All these lovely memories; so you can understand my shock when he would make embarrassing and inappropriate jokes and comments and didn't understand that they were wrong: he'd say things like 'You're getting a bit tubby Michelle' and 'Your hair looks bloody awful.' Dad would never normally have said such things.

John would get up in the middle of the night and dress in his suit, shirt and tie, announcing that he was off to the job he had left many years previously. Some nights I couldn't stop him from going out and it was an horrendous, exhausting and frightening task trying to entice him to come back inside from the dark cold night air. I would accompany John on daytime walks, in the hope of keeping him physically fit and trying to use up some of his energies, so that he would have better nights' sleep. It was like taking out a naughty toddler. I had to have eyes in the back of my head and pre-empt his every move. On one such walk he bent down, attracted by a large spherical shaped stone which was the size of a tennis ball. Before I could gather my senses, he had hurled it at the window of a house. Thankfully it just missed! Had the stone smashed the window, I would have had to knock at the door, not knowing what to expect, whilst desperately trying to explain this embarrassing situation. I never knew what was going to happen from one day to the next.

Sadly, even our walks had to be curtailed due to the numerous falls John started having in the house, and outside. He was so heavy to lift that sometimes I had to call an ambulance to help me get him up off the ground. The drugs he was prescribed led to uncontrollable shaking at times so he would lay, fallen, shuddering away, which alarmed the Good Samaritans who kindly offered to try and get him up.

We invested in a wheelchair but John hurled it out of the house in disgust. His violent disapproval also greeted the equipment which the physiotherapy team delivered, the rollator, two walking frames, a toilet frame, a commode and a bath board. It was frustrating to see these much-needed pieces of equipment lay discarded. Any attempts to incorporate them into our lives led to a battle of wills which John always won, due to his physical violence.

A tiny miracle occurred the day he finally accepted the wheelchair, which made my life so much easier, although he was extremely heavy to push around due to my slight build. I became very aware of all the broken pavements, high kerbs and hills that I had never previously noticed. John was in his element as he sat in his new throne – a perfect perch from which to shout his insults at the perplexed passers-by!

It felt like we had turned into a pair of recluses. If I did manage to entice him into the car for a trip to the local park, I would bitterly regret my actions when I couldn't get John back in the car to come home. How I appreciated the valued visits and support of our children; Michelle, Nick, and Mark. Their families were so understanding of the demands placed upon them too. Michelle reduced her work hours; she was such a godsend and she made it clear we were in this battle together. She shares her own sadness; my outgoing, gregarious dad had started to become anxious in the company of others, a ticking social time bomb who might suddenly pick a fight or demand to go home. Dementia stole his identity in more ways than you'd expect. When dad was first diagnosed, he could still follow a conversation, drive a car and go for a walk on his own. But the words 'vascular dementia' changed the way people treated him and the things he was allowed to do.

Of course, while people's perceptions changed instantly, everything else was an agonising drip of erosion. Things slipped bit by bit as dad became more childlike, and moody too. At first, he simply couldn't understand how to tie his shoelaces any longer. As time went on, he needed help to get dressed. He would get stuck inside his t-shirts and giggle at his own struggle – we would often find ourselves giggling together with him, but in actual fact we were terrified of dad's continued slide into helplessness.

Some of the memories of my dad make me laugh; some make me cry. As dad was losing his memory, I was gaining memories that I still cherish today. My dad would not have known it, but he left me a legacy, and for that I am thankful.

I remember the time we took dad to a local theatre to see cover band The Bootleg Beatles. He had always loved The Beatles back in the day. We thought it'd be a treat for dad to have an evening out listening to the timeless Beatles music. Big mistake! One of the symptoms of his dementia was the inability to differentiate what should and shouldn't be said aloud. 'What the bloody hell is this?' he said loudly as the music began. He sat grumbling and cursing; making it impossible for any of us to enjoy the show. We stayed for a short while, then took dad back to the car and drove home. Good intentions, not such a good outcome.

Dad and I went out on many walks together. I'd let him lead the way in an attempt to stir up memories. I remember one rainy day and he said, 'Come on, I'll take you round the back doubles'. I instantly knew the words 'back doubles' was dad's code name for a long walk. We linked arms under the big golf umbrella and we walked for miles in the pouring rain. Many familiar faces greeted dad while we were out. He was pretty well known around town, and many people in the neighbourhood knew him by name, particularly as he had taught so many of the locals to dance. He had a knack for recalling names and prided himself in the fact that he could greet people accordingly. As dad's dementia deepened, sadly, he couldn't reciprocate any longer. When people would come up to him, he'd say hello and give a smile, but then after they'd leave, he would ask who they were.

As passers-by came down our road John would often bang on the windows at them, shouting out that he was locked inside our house, being kept hostage. He also thumped walls, kicked the radiators and banged at the front door, angry that I had had to lock us both in for fear of him escaping.

It got to the stage where he would be throwing photo frames, ornaments and pictures across the room, as he shouted in anger at the television. I was scared out of my wits as he smashed two dining chairs against the wall. Thank goodness I was the other side of the opened rotary washing line the day he threw a heavy crystal vase out of the bedroom window, the shards of glass just missing me as it exploded on the ground. Where had all our toilet rolls gone? Out of the window, of course, along with the lovely ornamental robin which he'd cherished so much from Mark. I dreaded the reactions of the neighbours when our garden ornaments were hurled over the fence, along with his evening meal; I was so grateful that they were out so I could retrieve the dinner plus plate he had thrown over their fence!

John became incontinent and soaked bedsheets became a daily occurrence. I was exhausted from stripping the bed, washing, drying bedsheets and remaking the beds. Michelle helped as much as she could with difficult tasks, especially as I did not want to take my eyes off John for obvious reasons. I bought twin beds so single sheets were easier to cope with and I didn't get drenched in urine too. Even incontinence sheets and waterproof bedding failed to keep the bed dry so I am sure you can imagine the unpleasant stench!

John would rip incontinence pads off before hurling them across the room! He was so agitated by the things that his aggressive behaviour grew worse. One day I feared for my life as he pinned me against the wall, by my throat, and attempted to strangle me. I managed to squeeze out a whispered plea for my life, reminding John that we were husband and wife and we loved each other. Thankfully, he relinquished his grip and regained some recognition of who I was before he started to join me in my sobs. Small miracles did happen from time to time and John finally gave up the fight and accepted wearing the pads, more so when he became doubly incontinent.

It became a constant challenge to see past the disease, and to remember my real husband was the most loving affectionate man, who would never have done anything to upset or hurt me. The monster, who tried to push me down the stairs, on several occasions, was the incarnation of the vilest disease. It hurled shoes down at me as I scurried down the last few stairs trying to run to my safe hiding place, the cloakroom with its much-appreciated lock. I would sit quietly in the tiny dark locked room, curled up and sobbing, waiting for the storm to pass. I was petrified of what the beast, living in the shell of my beloved husband, was capable of inflicting on me. I could well understand how, in biblical times such unexplained behaviour changes would be explained away as demon possession; if only I could have had the devil living inside my wonderful husband exorcised. When I finally deemed it safe to leave my place of safety, I would find him sat in an armchair, totally oblivious to his earlier murder attempts as he innocently enquired as to where I had been.

John's faith still lived inside him. In more lucid moments John's frail voice would plead with God for a gun to kill himself. I would overhear his mutterings to God – prayers for help, telling God he wasn't well and that he was going doolally. He would be crying quietly as I wiped away my own tears at his simple confessions.

There were many dark days as I felt incapable of finding anyone to share these intimate moments with and besides, I was awash with many emotions including shame, hate and guilt. Of course, I had my wonderful children, but I did not want to further darken their memories of their dad by some of the horrific experiences I had encountered. I felt that I would be betraying my darling husband if I shared all the shocking incidents. It is only because I truly believe that someone out there will find their own comfort and inspiration to seek the relevant help, that I am now finding the courage to share my harrowing experiences.

Many friends had slowly disappeared over these dark years and Michelle points out how symbolic it was that the countless strings of Christmas cards had disappeared. It appeared that some friends just didn't care but we guess in reality they didn't know what to say when they saw the 'new John,' so they simply chose to stay away. Two of our dearest camping friends were supportive but John's ex work colleagues had vanished – although we do respect that others were aging and potentially experiencing their own health problems.

I used to have terrible nightmares that I was suffocating; I suppose my unconscious mind was trying to deal with how, in reality, my life was being smothered by the blanket of vascular dementia, there was no let up from the constant demands. I had become a prisoner held captive with an indefinite sentence. I didn't shout for help because I am of a placid and passive personality so everybody just assumed I was coping.

Michelle often raised her concerns about how exhausting and depressing it must have been having to run the home, cook the meals, sort out the problems, and provide care 24/7. Mum cared for dad single-handedly in their home for twelve years because of her calm nature and unconditional love. Dad had got rid of the carers – 'Get the hell out of here!' he would shout. Mum got a taste of freedom when dad attended the day centre for a year, until he got too loud and one afternoon when I collected him, I was greeted with the words – 'Can I have a word please, he's been very loud and disruptive in the group today,' Dad stopped going after that!

Normal life disappeared further when I gave up work in 2009. Sometimes Michelle, Nick and Mark did some dad sitting so I could get out for some much-needed respite; they were very supportive and I knew they were always there for me. We have always been a close family and this has helped us to survive throughout these heart-breaking years.

3. HOW DID IT ALL BEGIN?

S ome of the milder incidents, some of which we have recalled above, happened before the fateful day of which we are about to tell you. However, the more severe scenes, we have described, took place after this terrible day. You will understand how the awful events merged into one large grey cloud of doom through which the sun never completely broke through ever again. It becomes difficult to recall what happened when and in what order.

Sunday 11 March 2001 is a day that will be etched in our memories for evermore. John was doing what he loved doing, washing his precious car, when suddenly he collapsed. Our neighbour found him and called up to me through the open window where I was making our bed. I ran downstairs and we managed to get him up. He was dragging his feet and proceeded to projectile vomit several times. I called for an ambulance but by the time it arrived he appeared to have recovered. The paramedics gave him an ECG and checked his blood pressure which they recorded as normal. As he had been violently sick, the paramedics diagnosed food poisoning and it was left at that. John refused to go to hospital for further checks. However, the following morning, we noticed that his face was drooping on one side and his speech was rather incoherent.

Our GP arranged an emergency MRI scan and came to the family home to share the results. A white mass glared up at us, highlighted from the black background of John's brain. We were all in deep shock to hear that he had suffered irrevocable brain damage to both frontal lobes, both parietal lobes and intracranial haemorrhage bursts to large areas of the brain plus further widely scattered micro-haemorrhages and lobar haemorrhages. When the GP left John made no reference to the results and we have always wondered whether he was already at the stage where such important things didn't register.

The GP confirmed that John had suffered an Ischaemic stroke —Cerebral Amyloid Angiopathy, aged just 59. At this time the stroke diagnosis wasn't connected with dementia. However, John's memory and thinking slowly began to decline and as time went by, further neurological tests were carried out. It was not until 2006 when John was aged 64, that the official diagnosis of Vascular Dementia was made. John had always eaten healthily, exercised regularly and followed an active lifestyle. We stared in disbelief at the summary of his condition; Vascular Dementia, Alzheimer's / Frontal-Temporal Dementia / Pick's Disease.

We felt like a ship lost at sea in a deep fog as we were abandoned to find our way forward. We only had vague knowledge of this disease and assumed it just meant that John's memory would fade further; how wrong were we! Its many ugly faces soon leered at us with the darkening moods, aggressive and anti-social behaviour, cruelly disguising the John we all knew and loved.

I would visit a church and light candles for our parents, talking to them silently, wishing they were still alive to guide me through the trauma of it all. As part of the lengthy cognitive tests given to check John's mental abilities, such as memory and thinking, I remember how a clinical psychologist asked him to draw a clock and we were astonished when he drew the figures before the clock and when she asked him to draw a house, he drew the windows first. She explained this revealed that John had developed problems with spatial awareness. The following year, in 2007, John's driving licence was revoked. He was devastated beyond belief!

It was because of my unconditional love that I nursed John at home for as long as was humanly possible. Twelve long years took a terrible toll on my health. As it is, Michelle and I, who have decided, together, to share our story, you must forgive us when you hear our experiences more than those of the rest of the family. We have found it strangely therapeutic to lay all these years to rest by sharing our story. The John of old has re-emerged in our memories as we have recollected our stories. It will be an honour to the memory of a remarkable husband and dad, if just one reader gains comfort from our story – to realise that they are not alone, and that they will find a way to cope, just as we did.

Michelle explains the effects on relationships; I would have loved my future husband to ask my dad for my hand in marriage, as I am quite traditional. Sadly, this wasn't possible. My husband never knew dad before the vascular dementia took hold.

During the early years following the diagnosis the disease had not completely stolen John's awareness so it was traumatic to observe the times when he, himself, realised that things weren't how they should be. Michelle will never forget the tear-jerking moment, at her wedding, when her dad delivered his speech which I had written for him. I had typed it in large font on A4 paper. As John stood, he tapped his head and announced to all, 'I hope this bloody head of mine is going to let me get through this.' Michelle was naturally so proud of him but the moment had been tinged by the realisation that her dad was aware of his illness. We were thrilled that he was able to attend both Mark's and Nick's weddings a few years' later, and he appeared to be so happy. The boys were elated, in fact we all were.

The slight awareness he had that things weren't right led to depression and frustration when he realised he was incapable of simple tasks like tying his shoelaces and buttoning his shirts. Bouts of uncharacteristic anger made him lash out. These soon became everyday occurrences which we found embarrassing in public places. You might be surprised by the reactions of some of the public. He would shout and swear – we couldn't believe such words were even in his vocabulary. Some people understood, others clearly didn't as they expressed their disgust.

The rude remarks which burst from his lips were thankfully never directed towards children. However, we would cringe when an obese person passed as we knew what was coming as he called them – a fat bastard. John had always been inclusive and hated racism so we felt mortified when he made racial slurs. His patience had evaporated into thin air as he shouted at a lady in the supermarket, 'Get out of the way you silly old cow!' She would not accept my explanations about his dementia, instructing me to keep him under control or else she would call the manager! Another incident was that of a woman in the local park who did not react well to being informed that she was as ugly as her dog! I felt that I should have, 'Sorry,' tattooed on his forehead because we knew that he would have been devastated if he had known any of these vulgar words were ever to leave his mouth.

The perfect gentleman who respected everyone, who knew no social, racial, physical, religious or age barriers had treated everyone as his equal. He had been raised with immaculate manners which remained at his core until vascular dementia destroyed them. We were astounded that he even knew many of the words that had found their way into his mind, like the dreaded Japanese knotweed which overtakes and destroys gardens. Amazingly, he still knew never to use the 'F' word.

At one stage, John had been prescribed Diazepam to help curb his unpredictable bursts of anxiety and anger. One Friday afternoon, I had gone to the local chemist to collect the repeat prescription, only to be told 'Sorry madam, it appears to have gone astray.' I was mortified! This was the one and only drug that I knew I could rely on to keep John calm, and without it I was concerned that my life was in danger. Having explained the situation to the chemist, I managed to reach out to an emergency helpline that was able to issue me with three Diazepam pills to last the weekend!

We considered fleetingly that the best coping strategy could be laughter and to see the funny side of things. We tried to take a humorous approach when John embarrassed us in restaurants by banging his fists on the table, throwing the cutlery around as if seeking attention, like a naughty schoolboy, and then the clucking noises would start with his impressions of a chicken. However, we couldn't really sit there and laugh as the other diners and staff looked on in horror; we wished we'd all stayed at home. In fact, we asked for the bill and left as he continued to insult fellow diners, calling them a variety of names, 'fat bastard,' 'shit face,' 'ugly bugger.' We were definitely no longer into the idea of laughing our problems away!

We still went on holiday, although it was becoming increasingly difficult. On one occasion I had arranged a holiday abroad for us but when the taxi arrived to take us to the airport, John refused to get out of bed. The kind taxi driver hugged me as he read the disappointment, mixed with shame, stress and embarrassment all etched on my face.

I decided to call a halt to future coach trips when he felt the elderly passengers were not disembarking fast enough – 'Hurry up you stupid buggers, you should be in your coffins' he shouted. The guide was pointing out places of interest when John shouted out – 'Bloody hell, shut your gob, you silly old sod.' I realised that trying to lead a normal life was not going to work and that it was better for all concerned if we withdrew ourselves from society.

We couldn't become complete hermits, but even waiting in the doctor's surgery was agonising as John made his socially unacceptable comments. The busy lady doctor flew past us to reception. Her flip flops flopped as she dashed in wearing her beach-like attire of three-quarter length trousers and sleeveless top. As the patients followed her with their eyes, a voice popped up and no guessing whose voice it was! 'You'd think on a doctor's wage she could afford to wear a smart suit, stockings and a decent pair of shoes.' John's comment brought a few smiles in the waiting room and I couldn't help but wonder if they agreed!

Holiday fun in Italy.

John enjoying a spectacular view in Italy.

Proudly walking Michelle down the aisle.

A proud Dad at Mark's wedding

Congratulating Nick on his wedding day.

John and Vicky with our first-born grandchild.

The last 'best' photograph of John and Vicky.

4. THE SHOW GOES ON

The disease was relentless as it tormented us all with its latest shows! John began to hallucinate and he saw cauliflowers everywhere, guns on the worktop, strangers or friends in the room, behind him or in corners. It was disconcerting for us as we had to fathom if we were going to disagree or pretend that we saw them too.

I found it exhausting as John's pattern of sleep became even more disturbed. His gait changed and it was so sad to see the man who once strode out confidently, now shuffling around in his slippers. He was often drowsy and lethargic. How sad it was to find him staring blindly into space. After a staggered start to the disease, it became in full flow as we observed his lack of motor control. 'What are these for?' he would innocently ask when we presented him with a knife and fork at mealtimes.

It was arranged that a community mental health nurse would visit us regularly. She was an absolute godsend. I found it helpful to share experiences of the 'Memory Matters Groups' that she introduced us to. These sessions provided us with an opportunity to come together with other families affected by dementia.

Our community nurse also arranged for John to attend the day centre. How I enjoyed time to myself until he began to disrupt the quizzes, the games and music sessions with angry outbursts and verbal abuse and, as Michelle has explained, this all came to an end within the space of a year.

I joined local Alzheimer's meetings to chat with other carers but I found it disheartening when they shared their somewhat much milder experiences to me. So many carers expressed how their loved one would sit happily in a chair all day. John never sat happily in a chair all day! I felt increasingly isolated. I tried to accept the offer of personal care for John but it was a disaster from day one when he lashed out and shouted verbal abuse. 'Piss off,' he shouted, and they did.

We had learnt not to question John when he was living in the past. If he asked to visit his mum, who had passed away 24 years ago, aged 94, we would play along and say we would go after lunch; trusting by then he would have forgotten his request.

Michelle remembers one cold winter's day that turned out to be a nightmare. It was December 2009 and I was moving house and mum was reluctantly giving up a job she loved to care for dad full time. It was mum's last day at the estate agents. I remember feeling very ill at ease that we were leaving dad home alone for the day. As I was unpacking boxes, I had this horrible feeling that something bad was going to happen. At about 3pm it started to snow and at 6pm mum rang, 'Dad's gone missing!' Was I surprised? No! Was I worried? Yes!

Michelle arrived at ours to find her dad had disappeared, along with the brown paper package from the hallway which had been wrapped, waiting to be posted to her brother Mark. After fruitless searches of the local haunts, Michelle rang Mark, in the hope that John might have decided to go in person to deliver the parcel. He hadn't. Michelle then rang her brother Nick, to ask if dad had turned up there. He hadn't. Michelle, Mark and Nick then each went out, frantically driving in the thick snow searching the streets, looking for their dad.

I then called the Police who immediately alerted all train stations to London. Extra trains had been put on due to the heavy snow. As the snow was falling thick and fast, our troubled minds tormented us with visions of John laying, suffering from hypothermia. The hours ticked by until it was almost midnight! Still no John. It got to one in the morning and were losing hope, when suddenly the front door burst open and there was John, package under his arm, eager to tell us all about his day in London, meeting his ex-work friends. We were all so grateful to have him safely home.

John went missing several times. On one shopping trip I had to dash to the loo and John said he'd pop into the gents. I gave him strict instructions to stand still and wait for me if he was out first. On my return he was nowhere to be seen so I sent a kind obliging stranger into the gents to look for him. He had in fact been quite 'naughty,' and had chosen to wander off shopping instead but, thankfully, wandered back before I had too many kittens! He also wandered off in a bookshop – I had so many panic moments. I soon realised it was a good idea to leave a dementia card, with my contact details, in his pocket.

I can only keep repeating how John's disease had an effect on all the family. It seemed unfair that my three children, my 'Shining stars,' and their partners should have the burden of such stress, continually lurking in the background of their relationships. Nobody knew when the next crisis might erupt, when I might need to call them at inappropriate hours to come over and help. Michelle admitted that feelings of anger and resentment towards John's disease would sometimes rise up, followed immediately by guilt for even having such thoughts, but she was only voicing what the rest of us also felt at times. We all knew that we had no choice but to accept this new version of John.

COME ON IN

5. ACCEPTING HELP

I was utterly exhausted when I had finally agreed to my family's requests that I sought some respite care for John. When my beloved mum died from ovarian cancer in 1987, aged 64, I was offered counselling, but there had not been such offers as I struggled to care for John.

It broke my heart and made me feel very guilty when John went to reside in a care home for a short break. John proved to be a handful and the staff soon called to ask if we could collect the aggressive troublemaker who had thrown hot coffee over one of the staff. How difficult it was to refuse that request but we realised John was a danger to himself and safer, at that moment in time, in the hands of the professionals.

I had been advised to have John sectioned under the Mental Health Act, which meant he would have been detained in a psychiatric hospital. Looking back, it would have been much better for my health if I had accepted this advice at an earlier stage because I was absolutely shattered and often felt unsafe, but I was just not mentally ready to do this to my beloved husband.

By May 2013 John had lost the ability to walk. I moved his bed downstairs to the dining room when he began to have problems mounting the stairs. Crash mats, a hospital mattress and a bed guard were provided by the physiotherapy team. My own bed remained upstairs so I was exhausted from my runs up and down the stairs throughout the night; I hardly slept as I listened out for him. I know my family were worried that I would fall down the stairs in my dashes to attend to him. I was losing weight drastically; under seven stone I was looking quite frail myself.

His bed was in the dining room where he could look out into the garden, although we were not sure how much he could focus. We had a family celebration for one of the grandchildren's birthdays. Michelle offered to stay with me when all the family went home. John had soiled his pyjamas but he was heavy and past understanding any instructions. The two of us struggled to lift him to change his trousers and make him comfortable. We attempted to dry his pyjamas with a hairdryer and it suddenly hit Michelle how impossible things had become.

I eventually agreed to call John's community mental health nurse. Michelle travelled with him in the ambulance to the psychiatric hospital as I followed in the car. I wonder if we both subconsciously knew that he would never be returning home again. He was placed on 24 hours watch due to his physical violence – how ashamed the youthful John would be of the John he had become, but we all knew this abhorrent behaviour was the devil disease that had hijacked the mind of our perfect gentleman.

It took eight months for John's medication to be stabilised. A concoction of drugs was administered and we all felt so guilty leaving him there, but total physical and mental exhaustion had shown us that there was no other way. His unpredictable and violent behaviour could not be managed any longer without medication, plus the twenty-four-hour support of medically trained staff. He continued to lash out at staff; two or three staff were needed to restrain him, and on one reported occasion a team of seven staff were needed to calm his violent outburst. He grabbed a carer by her hair and banged her head on the bedside table. John had to be kept away from certain patients as he insulted their disabilities or physical appearance; we were all mortified to hear of such incidents and knew John would have never forgiven himself for these comments or actions had he been of sound mind.

In December 2013 he developed pneumonia and was just given a 30% chance of survival – his determination was still alive – against all the odds, he got better!

A Decision Support Tool (DST) was put into action to discuss the next steps in John's treatment. We finally heard the heartbreaking words we never wanted to hear, 'John won't ever be coming home.'

We put all our efforts into searching for a care home for him and secured a place where he had been for his respite care. His room was in the locked wing on the first floor. He could no longer walk but some of his fellow residents were often keen to exit the building. Many were vocal and often distressed. We never knew what to expect from one day to the next. The certainties were a bright and well lit day lounge, a faint smell of urine or bleach, mumbling television programmes, and constant bleeps that would often result in the care staff dashing to residents' rooms. There was no peace. The staff were amazing, going well beyond the call of duty, treating the residents as family. The home lovingly looked after John for five years. A sense of humour was definitely a necessity for any prospective staff and they would jokingly reprimand their naughty boy, John! The in-home music sessions were a great success with John. The percussion instruments provided an outlet for any built-up frustrations and there were lots of smiles when we were all asked to join in.

We soon settled into this new way of life with John; I visited him daily and the family visited whenever they could. The staff always ensured that it was a welcoming environment for us all with the tea, cakes and warm smiles.

John was a loving grandad and he would hold each tiny new grandchild, announcing that they were a little smasher! The grandchildren loved their visits to see raspberry blowing grandad – such great raspberry blowing contests took place and fun wheelchair rides! It was so refreshing to see the childish innocence that he shared with them as bubbles of happiness filled the room every time John spent time with his grandchildren.

"My name is Holly and I am three years old. This is a picture of me and grandad. Me and mummy go to the big house to see grandad. I am sad because grandad can't live with granny anymore because he is very poorly. Lots of kind nurses look after him in the big house.

My grandad can't talk a lot but he smiles and laughs and mummy takes lots of pictures of me with grandad and all our family so we will always remember our grandad.

Granny tells me that grandad was always happy and made everyone laugh. Granny says that grandad is her bestest friend forever.

I love my grandad very much."

A special bond between a grandad and his granddaughter,
Submitted and included in the Care Home Newsletter – April 2015.

Sadly, a day did finally arrive when we could no longer ignite a flicker of acknowledgement and his twinkle left his eyes, never to return. It was so sad to see the once active man hoisted from his bed to a hydro-tilt chair.

All the years of caring for John had taken a toll on my health and my body eventually declared that enough was enough and it was now time for it to be shown some care as I was rushed to hospital. I had contracted pneumonia and it was an extremely stressful time for my family as they now had two sick parents to visit. My body took a while to recover as my immune system had almost given up.

In early 2017 John had suffered a grand mal seizure which lasted an hour. I was summoned as the doctor doubted that he would survive. Our determined John proved the doctors wrong, yet again, with his miraculous recovery but, unfortunately, after that episode he was very susceptible to chest infections. He was given a nebulizer when his breathing became erratic.

John and family in the psychiatric hospital.

John always loved Christmas.

More Christmas fun!

John and Gromit!

John always enjoyed a slice of cake.

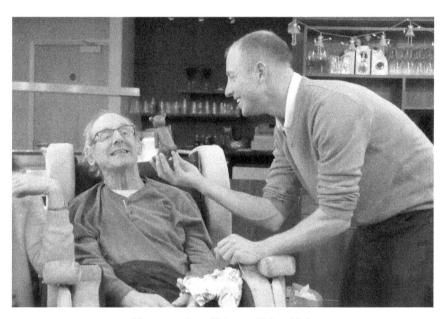

Happy to receive a Christmas gift from Mark.

Holly enjoying a ride with grandad in his big chair.

6. THE DARKEST DAYS

By 2018 John was suffering with increased chest infections. It was distressing to watch him wheeze and vomit. It broke my heart to read the sadness on his face as he stared blankly into space, the odd tear trickling down his cheek.

We'd bought a huge teddy bear, holding a heart, as a gift for John's 77th birthday but it lay on his bed, unnoticed by him. It felt like he was an empty shell and that 'our John,' had moved out. We no longer took the grandchildren to visit him as we did not want them to remember their grandad like this. We kept thinking that things couldn't get any worse but the real killer was still hiding away.

What does it mean for a person to die from vascular dementia? We knew that complications would occur that might be attributed as a trigger to the end, but we never really knew what to expect until we watched it for ourselves.

It was utterly heartbreaking to witness the real killer with dementia – witnessing John forget how to swallow. The food would go round and round his mouth but he couldn't remember the next steps. The nurses pureed his food and thickened his drinks to make it easier to swallow. He often refused the sippy cups which toddlers use – even in his advanced state. He would turn his head and purse his lips when we tried to get him to drink from the cup. We clung on to that. He may have been in the grips of the last stages, but by gosh, he wasn't going to lose what shred of dignity he still had by drinking from a plastic sippy cup!

One day he stopped eating and drinking completely. Not only does dementia make you forget how to swallow, but it also attacks the part of the brain that sends thirst and hunger pangs. And that's when we understood what would kill him – he would slowly wither away, dry up, unable and unwilling to eat and drink.

John developed another chest infection and we were informed that he would pass away before too long but nobody knew how long. He was gurgling when we came, a horrible gurgling cough as his lungs filled with mucus. He couldn't clear his throat, because he had forgotten how to cough, forgotten that coughing would clear the airways, that it was important to spit or swallow the phlegm. Instead, he spluttered which was extremely distressing to watch. Michelle likened it to an active Icelandic geyser that erupts naturally every 4-10 minutes! A nurse regularly performed a thoracotomy to relieve John's airways from phlegm.

It all moved quickly in slow motion from there. We decided, as a family, to allow nature to take its course because John had no quality of life left. We said no to ventilators, no to infection treatment, no to IV drips, but yes to the morphine drip which would keep him comfortable. We hadn't realised that this meant he would slip into deep slumber and we never saw him awake again. His heart was so strong that it continued to beat for thirteen days and nights after he last swallowed food or water. His morphine driver was adjusted, in minuscule increments, every day or two. We would comb his hair, moisturise his skin, moisten his lips, as we tenderly nursed him, whispering our pledges of love to him, in the hope that somehow, he would hear us. He was surrounded by love. It helped us. But whether or not it helped him we will never know.

We kept vigil by his bedside through his final days. It was awful listening to him struggling to breathe and feeling powerless to help. His temperate varied from high fever to chilled cold hands. His body was losing liquids, and so his heart had to pump faster to move the blood. 'The body is fighting the infection,' said the doctor. John's mouth was open and slack. Morphine makes all the muscles relax.

We played soothing church music and songs from Enya. The nurses had decided not to change his pad anymore – it wasn't necessary, and it was better not to disturb him. 'Let him go,' the nurse said, 'the less the living interfere, the easier it will be for him to separate and move on from life.' Surprisingly comforting words.

I got a phone call at 3am to come straight away, to not even change out of my nightwear. When I arrived, his condition had stabilised. What a fighter he was! We arranged for a Catholic priest to administer the last rights.

Michelle asked the doctor how he was going to die. What would cause his heart to stop? After so many days of not eating or drinking, there was no fluid left to go through his kidneys, which would stop working, and the toxins would build up. Eventually the toxins would reach a level that would impact his brain, combined with the fact that that there was less oxygen entering his bloodstream and more carbon dioxide building up. He would eventually stop breathing and his heart would slow to a halt. We were thankful for the morphine drip and how he seemed unaware of the dying process.

Michelle recalls, I wanted to stay longer with dad but it was snowing heavily so I decided to set off home. As I grappled with the heavy snowfall, it wasn't long before the traffic came to a standstill on the main road heading out of town. I found myself stranded and unable to move. How I wish I'd trusted my gut and stayed with my dad. I had an overwhelming feeling of impending doom. I knew I had to go back. I tried to turn the car around. My tyres were spinning. Two kind men got out of their vehicle to help me and I frantically explained, 'I've got to get to my dad, I don't want him to die alone!' They were pushing with all their might and eventually managed to get me moving. Thankfully, I made it to the bottom of the road to mum's and walked up the hill.

I was shattered, and so was mum. We sat quietly and drank hot soup. We turned the television on low and watched with total disregard. Suddenly, our thoughts were interrupted by the shrill sound of the telephone ringing.

A sombre voice uttered the words 'John has passed, I'm so sorry.' Nobody had been with him; mum and I believe that he wanted to be alone.

We trudged through the thick snow – to see John at peace in the home. A forget-me-not flower had been placed on the handle of the door to John's room. We timidly entered and bent to kiss the forehead of the man who had been the centre of our universe. The nurse stayed to welcome us and told us she'd been in two minutes before he passed, to moisten his lips; she said he was comfortable and he passed peacefully. We waited 4-5 hours for the undertakers, due to the snow. It was a surreal moment; we'll never forget watching him being taken away as we stood forlornly, surrounded by snow, in the still of the night.

'I'm so sorry. We all loved John,' rang out in our ears as the night nurse on duty joined us in a final farewell. We visited him in the chapel of rest several times.

Monday 11th March 2019 was the day we celebrated John's life at his funeral. We each knew that John would live on in our lives and that many of our future actions would be guided by all he had taught us. It was an extra special day because it was our 52nd wedding anniversary and ironically the day he had suffered the stroke. The lovely ceremony in the local church, with his favourite music, was followed by a beautiful spread of food at the wake. We kissed the coffin as it left for the crematorium. Donations raised over £1000 for Dementia UK. We live in hope that one day a cure will be found.

We interred John's ashes in a cemetery close to the family home. John's face often floats into my dreams. We each grieve in our own way. We especially think of him when a robin or butterfly joins us at our family gatherings, as they often do. John loved watching the birds feed from the bird feeder. When John first passed away, I would go to the cemetery every day to wipe his stone, to place and water flowers.

We thought of you today
But that is nothing new.
We thought about you yesterday
And days before that, too.
We think of you in silence.
We often speak your name.
Now all we have is memories
And your picture in a frame.
Your memory is our keepsake
With which we'll never part.
God has you in his keeping.
We have you in our heart.

7. WE FOUGHT. WE WON.

Michelle and I want others to benefit from our experiences, and we feel it is important to share the following information, which Michelle has prepared, to help you should your loved one need residential care.

When dad was moved into residential care in 2014 it was decided that he was eligible for NHS Continuing Healthcare, a fully-funded package of care that some people are entitled to receive as a result of disability, accident or illness. Dad's eligibility was based on the extent and nature of his care needs. Unlike local authority funding, it is not means tested.

Dad's vascular dementia meant that he couldn't communicate in any form, including letting carers know when he was in pain. He demonstrated challenging behaviour, such as aggression, for which he was given daily medication. He had a history of depression and anxiety, including hallucinations. He was agitated, totally confused and disorientated in time, place and person. He sighed and cried a lot and appeared restless, distressed and uncomfortable. He required full management of all aspects of personal hygiene needs. He was doubly incontinent. He was totally immobile and had spent the last three years being hoisted between bed and hydro-tilt chair, for which he required the full assistance of two carers. He was at high risk of pressure damage and skin breakdown. He was fed a pureed diet, was at high risk of choking and therefore needed to be monitored closely when eating. He suffered with constant bouts of vomiting undigested food. He had breathing problems and was regularly given an inhaler. He suffered ongoing chest infections. His declining mental capacity and tendency of violent outbursts made him a danger to himself, and those around him.

Each year, dad underwent a series of assessments from all relevant health and social care professionals, including a Deprivation of Liberty (DOLS) assessment that was carried out by a Section 12 Doctor and a Best Interest Assessor. Between 2014 – 2017 NHS Continuing Healthcare funding was awarded and paid.

Unbeknown to our family, In January 2017 an NHS Continuing Healthcare eligibility assessment had been called by the Clinical Commissioning Group (CCG). The Multi-Disciplinary Team (MDT) had gathered to assess dad's care needs in the Decision Support Tool (DST), a document the assessors used to 'score' dad's care needs in twelve different care domains. This was the crucial meeting to decide if dad's needs constituted a primary health need and therefore if he was still eligible for funding. Our family was excluded from dad's eligibility assessment, making it easier and quicker for them to get to a 'No'. We who knew dad's needs better than anyone else were denied the right to say that we disagreed with the assessor's views, and to have our disagreements recorded. No warning, no discussion, no consent!

In February 2017 the CCG informed us that dad's nursing needs had stabilised, and that his NHS Continuing Healthcare funding was to be withdrawn. It was as if he had miraculously got better! Mum picked up a letter from her doormat demanding fees for dad's care of £1400 per week! It is impossible to describe the distress and devastation this caused our family. How could the CCG have decided to leave my vulnerable dad without the nursing care and support he so desperately needed due to his rapidly deteriorating dementia?

The assessors had downplayed and ignored the evidence of dad's complex and unpredictable care needs. This was an extremely challenging time for our family. We were exhausted, depressed and burnt out, particularly as this came at a time when we were already experiencing stress and anxiety as our precious mum was in hospital suffering with pneumonia. I felt vulnerable, frightened and bewildered, not knowing which way to turn, but I knew I had to help my dad and challenge the ineligibility decision.

I spent hundreds of hours learning as much as I could about NHS Continuing Healthcare and started delving into the dark recesses of Continuing Care maladministration. I stumbled across two excellent resources that were to become a lifeline for our family:

1. **Beacon.** I called Beacon's free Information and Advice line and described my dad's situation. They arranged a free 30-minute phone consultation with me during which we discussed our family's options and the grounds on which we could demand a second MDT, this time with the family present. They helped us understand the eligibility criteria, navigate the assessment process, understand the DST and our assessment, and helped us write a powerful appeal backed by documented evidence.

2. **Care To Be Different** is a specialist online resource all about NHS Continuing Healthcare Funding in England. The information and resources shared on this website filled us with strength and confidence to counter what the NHS was telling us. We learned about Pamela Coughlan and the landmark Coughlan case at the Court of Appeal, and we quickly realised that my dad should, without doubt, be receiving NHS Continuing Healthcare funding to cover all his care fees.

These invaluable resources confirmed how the decision to remove dad's nursing care was cruel and a million miles away from what the NHS was created for, particularly as his need for nursing care came as a direct consequence of his disease. I lodged a formal complaint to the Patient Experience and Complaints Department, insisting that a repeat MDT meeting be arranged, this time with my family present. During the second meeting, many of the care domains were in dispute. It felt like we were having to describe dad's state of health to a team of NHS reps, whose main aim seemed to be to obstruct the funding process and deny him the care he was entitled to.

The meeting concluded that dad did not meet the eligibility criteria for NHS Continuing Healthcare funding and associated nursing care. We were told that dad's care plan would to be passed to the Local Authority for the provision of social care, including help getting up in the morning, getting dressed and washed, preparing meals, and managing social aspects of daily life. The assessment had rated dad's psychological and emotional needs as low and had failed to include sufficient mention of his violent behaviour towards carers and other care home residents.

We were told that our family would be means tested and charged for dad's care. Social Services sent a financial assessor round to visit mum, who helped himself to all her private financial files. Despite the talk of money to be paid by our family, we didn't pay the £5000 they demanded as arrears since the latest assessment for his care. We wrote to our local MP, Chief Executive of Health and Care for Hampshire County Council, the Director of Adults' Health and Care for Hampshire County Council and the Head of Legal Services for Hampshire County Council.

We appealed against the decision. Mum spent countless hours trawling through the paperwork, medical reports and DOLS reports, which portrayed the full extent of dad's needs within the twelve domains. All this documentation was submitted ahead of the MDT meeting. This meeting lasted laboriously for five hours and was led by a senior mental nurse, together with three social workers and two care home staff who faced Nick, Mark, Mum and I. A member of staff had pre-warned us that these meetings were like fighting with the dogs! Each of the care domains was grossly under-assessed. We challenged them on every domain by using our knowledge of the Coughlan case and explaining that dad's care needs matched, if not surpassed those of Pamela Coughlan.

As we awaited the results of this appeal, we were all nervous wrecks. Dad, my remarkable, capable father, had worked hard throughout his life, paying all his National Insurance contributions, never claiming a penny in benefits. We had invested effort into this appeal out of respect, love and honour, for the man who had always supported us. Now it was our turn to do all we could to maintain his dignity, quality of life and self-worth. We were outraged at the thought of having to pay for his care, as he lay dying in his bed.

Finally, the results came through in July 2017. Dad was deemed to be eligible for NHS Continuing Healthcare.

We finally proved that our strength was in our knowledge, our knowledge was our power to win, and we cannot stress sufficiently to our readers, how important it is to discover such knowledge by research.

The scandal of the way NHS Continuing Healthcare is managed is not just a funding controversy, it is about the misery and stress it causes at a time in life, which is already very sad and difficult, when you see the person you love, slowly degenerate. There is nothing transparent or fair about this system – the judge, jury and prosecutor are one and the same and the budget must be protected, no matter the cost. It is shameful.

We also want to share with readers, that it is essential to seek both financial, and health and welfare lasting power of attorney. We were wrongly advised by a highly respected solicitor, and upon his advice, we had not applied for the health and welfare lasting power of attorney. Due to this, we were refused any input into decisions over dad's everyday healthcare and medical treatments. Nor were we consulted about discussions between the residential home and health and social care staff.

Our family's message to anyone who has a relative in care and paying care fees is simple: challenge everything you are told and don't take no for an answer.

COME ON IN

8. TEN KEY POINTS

Michelle and I have tried to think of some helpful points which might help you if you are embarking on a journey like ours.

1. **Call 999 immediately.** If someone collapses with a suspected stroke, call for an ambulance and insist on hospital admission. Ischaemic strokes can often be treated using injections of a medicine called alteplase, which dissolves blood clots and restores blood flow to the brain.

2. **Lasting Power of Attorney (LPA).** Gives you control to appoint someone you trust to make decisions on your behalf, as if you were making them yourself. To make both medical and financial decisions, we recommend you select both Property and Financial Affairs plus Health and Welfare.

3. **Evidence is key.** Keep a diary of the care and supervision you are providing on a daily basis, as the evidence gained will highlight the intensity.

4. **RADAR Key** (also known as National Key Scheme). Get access to UK public toilets designed for disabled people. Contact Adult Services.

5. **NHS Continuing Healthcare.** To be eligible, your care needs must be primarily 'healthcare needs' (and the responsibility of the NHS) and beyond the scope of local authority social care services.

6. **Identification.** Dementia patients and carers should carry identification with emergency contact details. When travelling have details of the travel company, resort/hotel details in the pockets of the patient.

7. **'No cold callers' sign.** Protect yourself and dementia sufferers by fixing a large sign on the front door to keep unwanted callers away.

8. **Telephone Preference Service.** Register to stop marketing/scam calls and limit the number of credit/debit/store cards carried.

9. **Always agree.** Patients with dementia can be confused concerning reality so it is helpful to always agree with the patient when they insist, for example, their parents are still alive. Never argue, it will just lead to increased confrontation. Distract the patient if possible. Keep conversations easy. Choose easy watching television, variety shows, enjoyable programmes, play fun but simple board games and jigsaws but accept when the patient loses the ability to do this.

10. **Never force feed.** Serve smaller portions and remove food if not wanted.

9. ONWARDS AND UPWARDS

John had been under the grip of vascular dementia for eighteen long years; it might have stolen his freedom and eventually his life but the two things it could not take were our happy memories, although it did try to bury them, and our unconditional love. We appreciate our memories slowly resurfacing of the John prior to the illness. They warm our hearts as they float back in at the most unexpected moments; for me, memories of a romantic husband who treated me with kindness and respect. We always enjoyed the little things in life such as snuggling next to each other on our sofa to watch the television. Looking back I realise that this was actually a big thing!

Some people seemed to think that our grief might have been less as we had time to grow used to losing John, step by step, but nothing could be further from the truth. The grief was as raw as if he had suddenly dropped dead after a healthy life. We all still miss him so much. John and I had a close relationship, soulmates, we did everything together. It will always haunt me that the home staff told me that, in the early days when he was able, John always asked where I was.

When Michelle and I decided to write this book together, we both decided it would be nice to spend a weekend away where we could reflect and work upon our plan. We chose the beautiful city of York, and as we chatted over our memories and our hopes and dreams for our book, it felt like John was with us as we giggled over the hilarious, though sometimes heart-rending moments. We felt a sort of healing was taking place, setting us free to move forward with positivity, sharing John's story and our journey with others in order to support them.

As we explored York Minster, we could almost hear John's voice – he would have loved that magnificent building because, as we have referred, he used to love architecture. During his illness, Michelle and I took John on a mini-break to Exeter where we had explored the cathedral and he was in awe of it. He was in a wheelchair then but was completely mesmerised, just as he had been on that visit to Italy when he had explored the wonderful churches and cathedrals.

What a wonderful mother and daughter weekend we shared, going to the cinema to see the latest Downton Abbey film, exploring the city walls, enjoying the sights by open top bus. It was quite therapeutic to realise, if it hadn't been for John's illness, these particular special moments would not have been happening. We realised that out of our devastation, positivity could rise. We still have John's love, integrity, core values, sense of humour, appreciation of family, so many qualities that guide us today – he'll always be with us and the pages of this book will ensure that future generations will know John too. Since he passed away, we have all found our ways of continuing our lives. I've been to Yoga and Zumba, meeting new acquaintances, and I am finding some closure as Michelle and I write this book. Michelle has completed all her assignments for her CIM in Professional Digital Marketing and will graduate at Westminster. John would have been so proud of her as he was when she graduated from university.

As a family we have participated in annual sponsored walks to raise awareness of dementia, when we all had special memories pinned to our backs. Each of us treasure the teddy bears we had made from his favourite clothes.

As a family we each have our individual memories of John and our own ways in which we keep him with us in our lives. He has influenced each of us in so many ways which we share here in our personal thoughts:

Walking for John at our annual memory walks.

Memory bears made from John's favourite clothes
– waiting to go home with granny and the grandchildren.

We will always remember the good times.

Michelle

Dad was the man who held me when I was a child. The man who came to watch me perform in my school plays. The man who helped me build snowmen and took me sledging on snowy days. The man who took me on fun summer holidays. The man who treated me to a bag of chips on weekend days out. The man all my friends loved. The man who helped me buy my first car. The man who nearly burst with pride when I graduated from university. The man who walked me down the aisle on my wedding day. The man I enjoyed drinking tea and whisky with. The man I belly- laughed with over the silliest of things. The man who made me happy when I was sad. The man who loved me no matter what. The man who helped shape me into the person I am today.

I was never a natural when it came to standing up to authority – until 2017 when I faced the 'fight of my life' in pursuing the NHS to take good care of my dad in his 'darkest hour'. I fought valiantly for Dad, showing courage, resilience and staying power against ever-lengthening odds. And when I reflect, I realise that these are all qualities that I inherited from Dad.

Dad's dementia diagnosis undoubtedly altered our family's life plans, but I refuse to let the manner of his death define him. My Dad was way more than dementia disease and in my truest, happiest memories of him, dementia doesn't even feature.

Nick

We all learn from our elders, and for dad, this was no exception. From having impeccable attention to detail with a spot of OCD, the pursuit of excellence, the ability of simply getting things done, working hard and being self-motivated to achieve these goals, never accepting second best, thinking of others, and always willing to go the extra mile – especially for strangers – without expecting anything in return. Michelle, Mark and I possess all of these qualities in abundance and these values all came from our parents.

The biggest lesson learned from Dad's early passing is to spend your time and energy on things that matter. Not to get caught up in the rat-race of life but instead prioritise time with your family and your health over work and stuff. And to do it now, rather than wait until retirement, that may never come.

Mark

I like to remember the good times with Dad. He loved spending time with the family, walking, cycling and dancing. He especially enjoyed going on camping trips which I take a great deal of pleasure in now doing with my own family. He loved listening to country and western music which I often listen to in my work van as a reminder of him.

Dad was always there to help me when I needed it most. He would help me to fix my bike and help me to get back up when I fell off it, help me with my homework, help me through my teenage years, help me to buy my first car and help me to drive it, help me to find a job, help me to buy a house, help me to be a father and most of all, help me to be myself.

Dad loved a bit of DIY at home, his attention to detail was amazing. When we needed a new bathroom at the family home, I offered to help install the new suite. Dad was there every day checking in on me. It was great to spend time together working out how to get it just right and his favourite phrase was, 'Are we winning?' My response of, 'Yes Dad, we're winning' always put a smile on his face.

Although Dad was taken from us earlier than anyone would have expected, I'm so grateful he got to see Michelle, Nick and myself on each of our wedding days and to meet his six wonderful grandchildren. He was a proud dad and grandad!

Vicky

I look up towards the sky, in the still of the night with wonder. I silently muse, with an aura of curiosity, as I feel his presence around me. Could one of those twinkling array of stars perhaps be my husband watching over me? My mind drifts back in time…

How can I forget the abundance of happy times we shared together, his inspirational character and kind caring nature, and that beaming smile. How can I forget those priceless moments on the births of our children, that he was 'there' each time, waiting to take the little one in his arms, overwhelmed with love and emotion. How can I forget so many enjoyable family times, the fun-filled holidays, the birthdays and all the festive Christmas times we shared with our entire family, oozing with fun and laughter, and the friends of all ages, just popping in. We welcomed everybody.

John was by far my best friend and soul mate, a good husband, dad, and grandad, and he worked hard. Together, we nurtured our children to become the fine adults they are today, always 'there' for one another, combining a perfect balance of work and leisure for their own families.

John was a proud dad, and what a wonderful legacy he leaves behind in our six adorable grandchildren. They are an utter delight to know, and to love, forever happy, making us laugh, just like their grandad. I will never forget our precious memories. They are valuable treasures, and which nobody can take away.

John lost his freedom but never our love. As we heal, we rediscover our freedom and by doing so we hope to offer you ways in which to maintain your own.

CPSIA information can be obtained
at www.ICGtesting.com
Printed in the USA
BVHW051209110123
656079BV00014B/487